KATHERINE AND HUGH COLLEDGE

WAGGON WHEELS

26 PIECES FOR VIOLIN PLAYERS

BOOSEY & HAWKES

In this collection of pieces for beginners, we have adopted a 'slowly but surely' approach. By gradually introducing new ideas and giving several examples to illustrate each point, the student has the opportunity to consolidate newly-acquired skills and build a firm foundation for future learning.

This book – which is a sequel to *Stepping Stones* – covers 2nd, 3rd and 4th fingers (in 1–23–4 pattern) and slurred bowing.

In order to keep the music as simple as possible, expression marks and so on have been omitted from the violin part until *Hills and dales* onwards but – of course – teachers and pupils may always add their own.

With one exception, the piano introductions are optional. Except in *With an upbeat*, introductory 'rest' bars have not been included in the violin part, although the length of the introduction is indicated at the top of each piece. For this reason, in Nos 13, 20 and 26, the *DC al Fine* in the violin part corresponds with the *DS al fine* in the piano part.

KATHERINE & HUGH COLLEDGE
London, UK

Kathy and Hugh met in East London where they both worked as peripatetic teachers at Newham Academy of Music. Hugh had previously studied oboe and piano at Trinity College London while Kathy was a violin student at NE Essex Technical College (now Colchester Institute). They were both born in London but Kathy started to play the violin in New Zealand where she lived in her youth.

Their association with Boosey and Hawkes began in the 1980s when the couple added to the pieces Kathy had written for her pupils in Newham to create *Stepping Stones* and *Waggon Wheels*. They later added *Fast Forward* and *Shooting Stars*, as well as a number of works for beginner string ensemble in the *Simply 4 Strings* series. More recently they contributed two new string quartets to the *4 Strings* series edited by Liz Partridge.

They moved to Norfolk in 1995 and continued to teach in the State and Independent sectors until their retirement.

Published by Boosey & Hawkes Music Publishers Ltd
Aldwych House
71–91 Aldwych
London
WC2B 4HN

www.boosey.com

© Copyright 2021 by Boosey & Hawkes Music Publishers Ltd

ISMN 979-0-060-13827-0 | ISBN 978-1-78454-646-5 (violin part)
ISMN 979-0-060-13553-8 | ISBN 978-1-78454-477-5 (violin part & piano accompaniment)

Printed by Halstan:
Halstan UK, 2–10 Plantation Road, Amersham, Bucks, HP6 6HJ. United Kingdom
Halstan DE, Weißliliengasse 4, 55116 Mainz. Germany

Piano performance and audio production by Robin Bigwood
Violin performance by Alexandra Wood

Music origination by Moira Roach

Cover illustrations by Jo Moore
Cover design by Chloë Alexander Design

WAGGON WHEELS

26 PIECES FOR VIOLIN PLAYERS

AUDIO RESOURCES

Stream or download audio for this book via the weblink below
or scan the QR code

https://audio.boosey.com/Tdsu

WAGGON WHEELS | Katherine & Hugh Colledge
Copyright © 1988, 2018 by Boosey & Hawkes Music Publishers Ltd

1. In a garden

Count 4 bars

2. Summer breeze

Count 2 bars

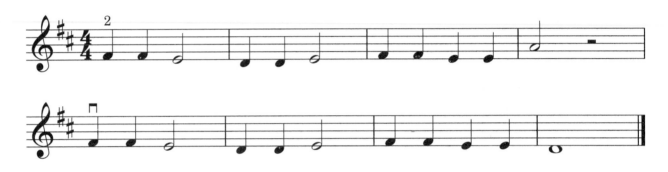

3. Goldfish bowl

Count 2 bars

4. **Penny-farthing**

Count 2 bars

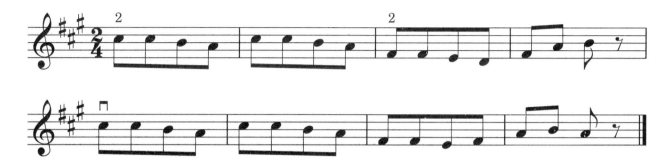

5. **Butterflies**

Count 4 bars

6. **Westminster Abbey**

Count 2 bars

7. Dinosaurs

Count 2 bars

8. Paddle steamer

Count 2 bars

9. Waterfall

Count 2 bars

10. Knickerbocker glory

Count 2 bars

11. Hills and dales

Count 4 bars

12. Upstairs, downstairs

Count 2 bars

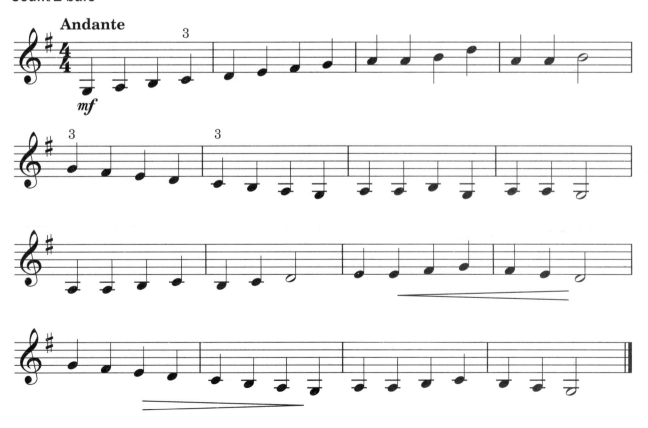

13. Daydreaming

Count 2 bars

14. Bell-ringers

Count 4 bars

15. Polka dots

Count 4 bars

16. Nightingale

Count 2 bars

17. Chinese lanterns

Count 4 bars

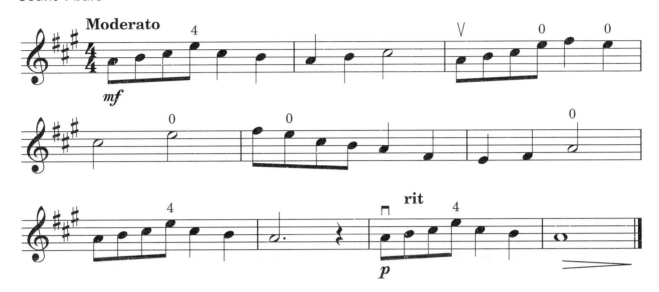

18. Fiddlesticks

Count 4 bars

WAGGON WHEELS | Katherine & Hugh Colledge
Copyright © 1988, 2018 by Boosey & Hawkes Music Publishers Ltd

19. Windscreen wipers

Count 4 bars

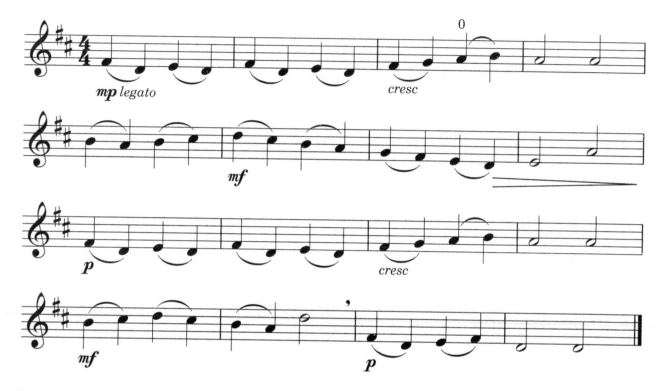

20. Bow ties!

Count 4 bars

21. Ice dancers

Count 4 bars

22. Full moon

Count 4 bars

23. Waggon wheels

Count 2 bars

24. With an upbeat

25. On the wing

Count 2 bars

26. Lollipop man

Count 2 bars